Practice Tests for
Key Stage 2
Mathematics

Peter Patilla

Oxford University Press

Acknowledgements
Many thanks to the editorial team at
Aldridge Press: Charlotte Rolfe, Sarah
Henderson, Felix Muriithi, Sheila Dampney,
Jocelyne and David.

Oxford University Press, Great Clarendon Street,
Oxford OX2 6DP

Oxford New York
Athens Auckland Bangkok Bogota Bombay
Buenos Aires Calcutta Cape Town Dar es Salaam
Delhi Florence Hong Kong Istanbul Karachi
Kuala Lumpur Madras Madrid Melbourne
Mexico City Nairobi Paris Singapore
Taipei Tokyo Toronto

and associated companies in
Berlin Ibadan

Oxford is a trade mark of Oxford University Press

© Peter Patilla 1996
First published 1996
Reprinted 1997

ISBN 0 19 838195 6

Designed by Geoffrey Wadsley
Illustrations by Barking Dog Art
Packaged by Aldridge Press

Printed in Hong Kong

• Contents •

What are the Key Stage 2 Tests?

- In England, Wales and Northern Ireland all pupils aged between 10 and 11 must take a National Test in three subjects: English, Mathematics and Science. The results of these tests will be reported to parents and passed on to the next school.

- The National Curriculum is divided into Levels matched to ability. Level 1 is the starting point for children aged 5, and Level 10 for very able 16-year-olds. The average level reached by an 11-year-old child should be Level 4, although a few very able children will reach Level 6. Most children will be working on Levels 4 and 5 when they are in Year 6 and aged 10 to 11.

- The National Curriculum tests for Mathematics taken by children in school cover Levels 3 to 5 with a special Level 6 test taken by the most able.

How can this book help?

- This book has been designed for children aged 10–11, to help them prepare before being assessed by the national tests. The questions in each test will give valuable practice for these National Curriculum tests and will give you information about how well your child is getting on with National Curriculum mathematics.

- The tests cover Levels 3 to 6 of the National Curriculum with particular emphasis on Levels 4 and 5.

- The mathematics work being tested in this book covers Number and Algebra, Shape and Measures, and Handling Data and matches what is covered in the national tests.

- The chart on pages 62 and 63 shows how each question relates to each of these three mathematical areas. It can also be used to show where your child needs more help and practice.

Using this book

- There are 7 tests in this book. Each test should take your child about 30 minutes to complete, but don't rush or pressurize them. Encourage them to do as much as possible but allow them to stop when they want to – remember that these are only practice tests.
- You can give some help to your child if they seem unsure as to what to do, provided this help does not extend to giving the answer or showing them how to reach the answer. The help should be confined to encouraging and reassuring them and confirming what they have to do.

Materials needed

- pencil, rubber and a centimetre ruler.
- simple calculator.
- It might be helpful to have tracing paper, or greaseproof paper available to help with a few of the shape questions.

Instructions to your child

- Write the start and finish times on the test and encourage your child to work swiftly but carefully through the test.
- Read all the questions very carefully. Look at the pictures and diagrams because they are part of the test.
- The main parts of all the questions are in coloured boxes and the pencil shows where to write your answer or any working out.
- The questions get more difficult as you work through each test. Try all the questions but if you can't do one don't worry, just move on to the next question. At the end of the test go back, check your answers and have another go at any questions you found difficult the first time.
- When there is a calculator picture with a cross through it you must not use a calculator at all. A calculator picture with a tick on it means a calculator should be used to answer the question. If there is no calculator picture a calculator may be used.
- There is room for working out on the test, so do not write on extra bits of paper. You must show any working out you do.

Marking the tests

- The answers are on pages 55 to 61.
- At the end of each set of answers is a guide to the mathematical level your child has achieved on that test.
- Encourage and reassure your child: confidence is an important factor when sitting for any test.

Finding your child's level

- An approximate level is found at the end of the answers to each test, and this gives an indication of how your child has done. A more accurate assessment can be obtained by adding the results of all the tests on the Test Record (page 64).
- This overall calculation will indicate whether your child has achieved Level 3, 4 or 5 of the National Curriculum in these tests. For very able children it will show whether they are beginning to work at Level 6.
- It is important to remember that mathematics at Levels 4 and 5 is quite demanding for children aged 10 to 11 and that the national average is about Level 4. Any child reaching Level 5 is doing very well indeed.
- Use the chart on pages 62/3 as a guide to giving your child extra help. The chart shows both the level and the mathematical area being assessed.

Teacher assessment

Not all the mathematics work covered in schools as part of the National Curriculum is tested through pencil and paper tests. Teachers will use their experience and expertise to assess your child in these areas and add this information to the test results to give a final mathematical level for your child.

• **Test 1** •

1 This machine multiplies all numbers by 5.

6 in ⟶ 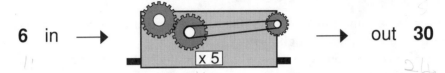 ⟶ out **30**

x 5

Finish the table.

in	2	4		
out			35	50

2 These potatoes are being weighed.

kg

0 2 4 6 8

Write the weight of the potatoes.

kg

3 Write which numbers the arrows point to.

500   1000

PAGE TOTAL

4

One ounce is about the same weight as 30 grams.

Write how many ounces are about the same as 270 grams.

 ounces

5

Write how many days there are in seven weeks.

days

6

Join another pair of numbers which has a difference of 6.
Do not join diagonal numbers.

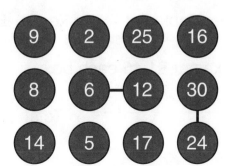

PAGE
TOTAL

7 Numbers are missing from the chain.

Write the missing numbers in order.

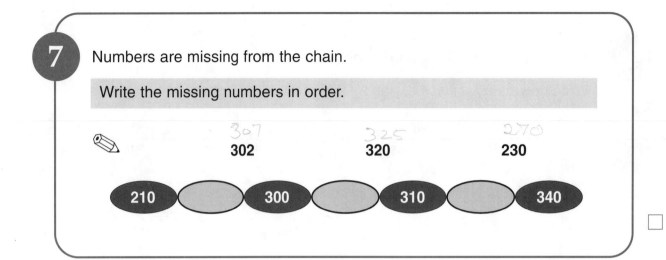

307   325   270
302   **320**   **230**

210   300   310   340

8 Write how many degrees the temperature has risen.

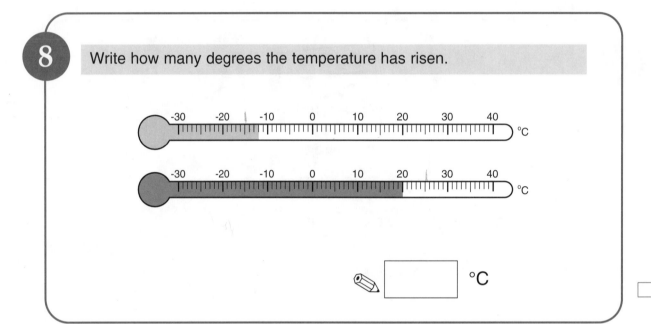

°C

9 Fill in the missing totals.

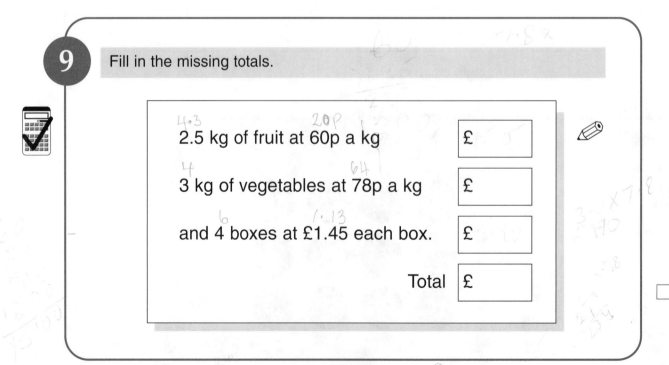

4·3   20p
2.5 kg of fruit at 60p a kg   £

4   64
3 kg of vegetables at 78p a kg   £

6   1·13
and 4 boxes at £1.45 each box.   £

Total   £

PAGE TOTAL

10 Draw 2 lines of symmetry on each shape.

  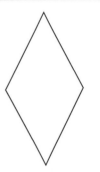

11

Lonster to Dibling					
Monday to Friday		**Saturdays**		**Sundays**	
Lonster	Dibling	Lonster	Dibling	Lonster	Dibling
depart	arrive	depart	arrive	depart	arrive
0700	0845	0700	0840	0830	1110
0800	0945	0830	1015	1130	1354
0900	1047	1000	1145	1330	1540
1000	1141	1130	1310	1530	1732
1100	1255	1300	1440	1705	1850
1200	1350	1430	1615	1805	1960
1300	1450	1600	1740		
1400	1560	1700	1840		
1500	1645	1800	1940		
1600	1740				
1700	1830				

Write the time a train must leave Lonster to arrive in Dibling at 1440 on a Saturday.

12 Measure the length of this pen.

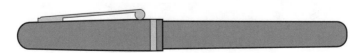

 Length = ☐ cm

PAGE TOTAL

13

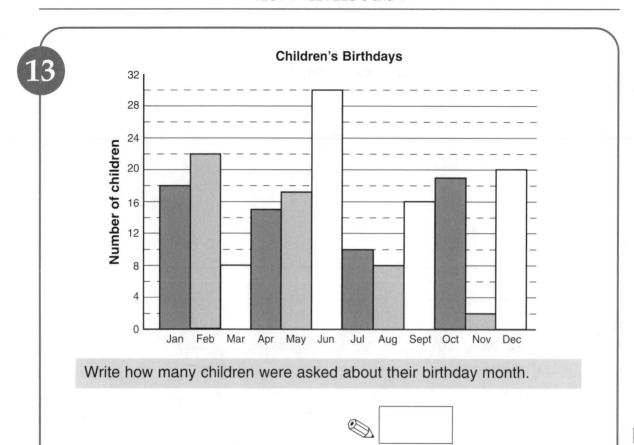

Children's Birthdays

Write how many children were asked about their birthday month.

14 Write numbers on the calculator keys to make the answer 56.

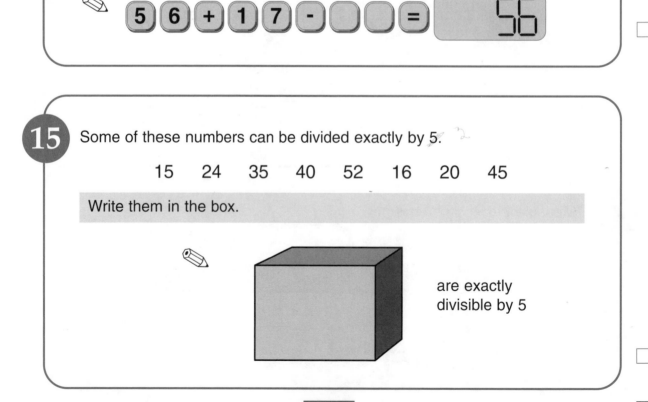

15 Some of these numbers can be divided exactly by 5.

15   24   35   40   52   16   20   45

Write them in the box.

are exactly
divisible by 5

PAGE
TOTAL

16 The clocks show the beginning and end of lunch.

Write how long the meal took.

 minutes

17 Answer this sum.

$$4.56 + 3.24 - 1.95 = \boxed{}$$

18

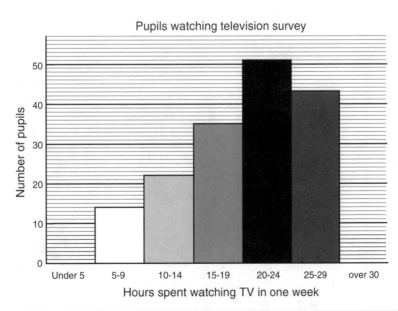

Pupils watching television survey

Number of pupils / Hours spent watching TV in one week

Write how many pupils watched between 15 and 19 hours of TV.

PAGE TOTAL

19 Tick the road signs which have rotational symmetry.

☐ ☐ ☐ ☐ ☐

☐

20 Here is a map.

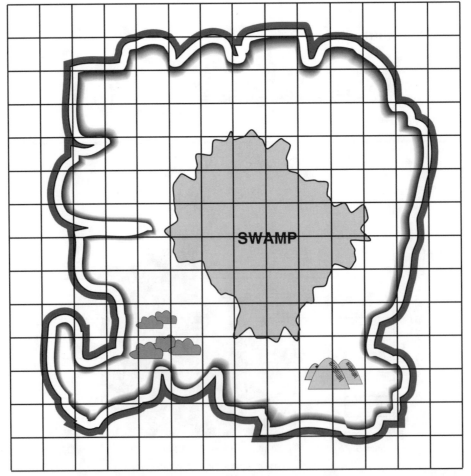

Estimate the area of the swamp.

 squares

☐

PAGE TOTAL

• Test 2 •

Time started [:]
Time finished [:]

1 Lee and Hassim are playing with old tickets.

312 LONDON BUS COMPANY 80P

320 LONDON BUS COMPANY 80P

302 LONDON BUS COMPANY 80P

331 LONDON BUS COMPANY 80P

322 LONDON BUS COMPANY 80P

Write the five ticket numbers in order, smallest first.

[   ] [   ] [   ] [   ] [   ]

2 Write how much water is in the jug.

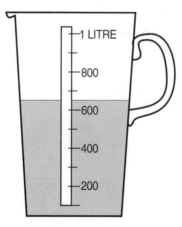

1 LITRE
800
600
400
200

 [   ] ml

3 The calculator shows the total of a bill.

Write this amount in pounds.

3.2

£ [   ]

PAGE TOTAL

4 This egg box holds 10 eggs.

Write how many boxes will be needed for 78 eggs.

 boxes

5 Fran cuts three lengths of wood from a 320 cm long plank.
The three pieces measure 98 cm, 126 cm and 48 cm.

Use a calculator to find the length left from the 320 cm plank.

6 Thomas was adding up on his calculator. He pressed +7 by mistake.

Write the key presses he must use to undo the addition.

PAGE
TOTAL

7

Gita and Jo were flipping tiddlywinks.
Gita flipped her tiddlywink 147 cm and Jo flipped his 82 cm.

Put a cross on the line to show Jo's tiddlywink.

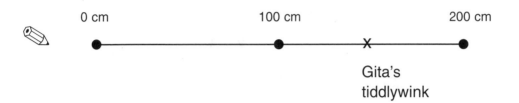

0 cm   100 cm   200 cm

Gita's
tiddlywink

8

Here is a line of numbers.

Find which two of the numbers total 83 and draw a ring round them.

17   27   36   42   47   50   69

9

Here is a number cross with four numbers missing.
The three numbers across must total 90 and so must the three numbers down.

Write the numbers 20, 30, 40 and 50 in the circles to make the correct totals.

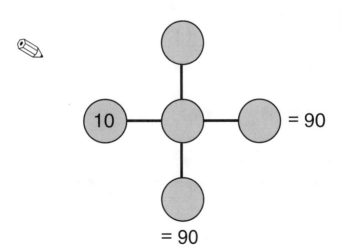

10   = 90

= 90

PAGE TOTAL

10 Write + − x or ÷ in the box to make the sum correct.

6 x 4 ☐ 3 = 8

11 Kerry bought 17 books at a car boot sale. Each book cost 9p.
She used the fact that 9p = 10p − 1p to work out the cost.

Show how she worked out how much to pay.

12 Write what all of these shapes have in common.

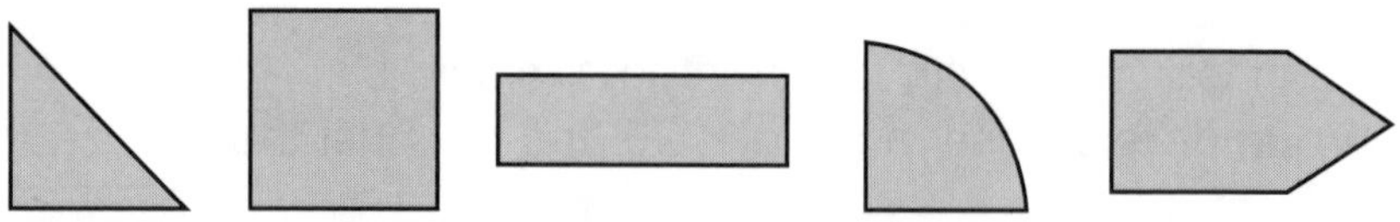

_____

_____

13 Measure the length of this ribbon.

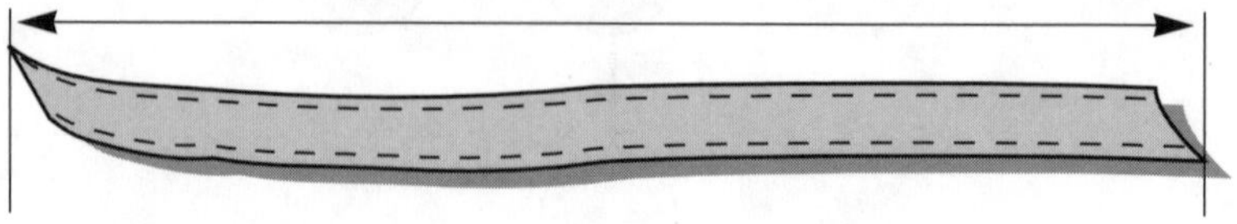

Length = ☐ cm

PAGE TOTAL

14 This chart shows a traffic survey carried out over one week outside a village school. The survey was started at noon each day and lasted for one hour.

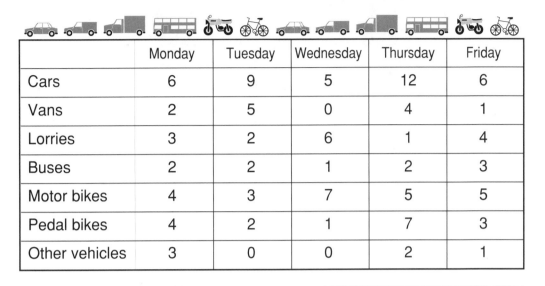

	Monday	Tuesday	Wednesday	Thursday	Friday
Cars	6	9	5	12	6
Vans	2	5	0	4	1
Lorries	3	2	6	1	4
Buses	2	2	1	2	3
Motor bikes	4	3	7	5	5
Pedal bikes	4	2	1	7	3
Other vehicles	3	0	0	2	1

Write how many vehicles were counted on Thursday.

 vehicles

15 The graph shows how many cars passed school in town between noon and 1.00pm during one week.

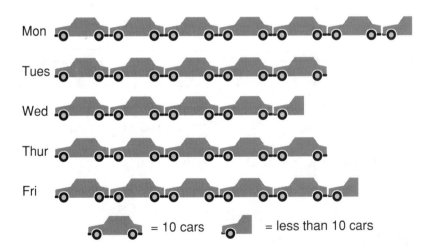

Mon

Tues

Wed

Thur

Fri

= 10 cars   = less than 10 cars

Write the day on which between 50 and 60 cars passed by.

PAGE TOTAL

16 This machine finds one quarter of numbers.

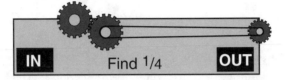

IN   Find 1/4   OUT

Complete the table.

In	Out
16	4
48	

17 Sonya is finding the perimeter of her lawn in strides.

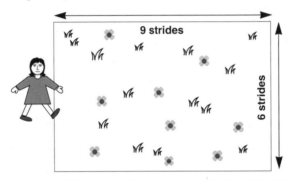

9 strides

6 strides

Write the perimeter of the lawn in strides.

[ ] strides

18 Look at Sonya's lawn in question 17. She measured her stride as 83 cm.

Work out the length and width of the lawn in cm.

[ ] cm

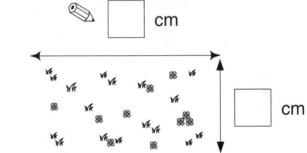

[ ] cm

PAGE
TOTAL

19 These three shapes are identical. They are the same shape and size.

Tick all the triangles which are identical to triangle A.

 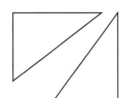 

20 Here is a graph to show how many bricks Andrew laid one morning.

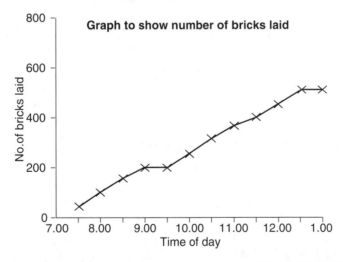

Graph to show number of bricks laid

Write the start and finish times of his early morning break.

PAGE TOTAL

• Test 3 •

Time started

Time finished

1   Write in the missing number.

 $\boxed{} \div 5 = 23$

2   This machine multiplies all numbers by 4 then adds 5.

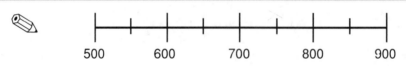

8 in ⟶ [×4] ⟶ [+5] ⟶ out **37**

Finish the table.

in	6.	9		
out			33	45

3   Mark with a cross the number 725.

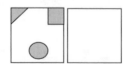

500   600   700   800   900

4   This picture shows half a symmetrical pattern.

Tick the picture which shows the other half.

PAGE TOTAL

5

The table shows how many labels were collected by five pupils.

	Monday	Tuesday	Wednesday	Thursday	Friday
Petra	9	8	4	5	3
Thomas	2	5	0	7	6
Kapil	3	9	3	8	8
Lisa	4	6	9	9	2
Fran	0	6	2	3	5

Write who collected most labels on Tuesday.

6

Simon thinks of a number.

If I add 36 to it, I get 72.

Write Simon's number.

7

Write in the missing digits.

```
    2 □ 8
  + 3 7 □
  _____
    6 4 4
```

PAGE TOTAL

8 There is a sale at the shoe shop. They have 50% off the marked prices.

Full price **£30**

Write the sale price of the shoes.

9 This sum has the same number missing from each box.

Write the missing number in the boxes.

 ☐ x ☐ + ☐ = 30

10 There is a cross at (2,1). Follow these instructions.

Start at (2,1) and draw a straight line to (4,5).
Draw a straight line from (4,5) to (5,2).
Draw a straight line from (5,2) to (2,1).

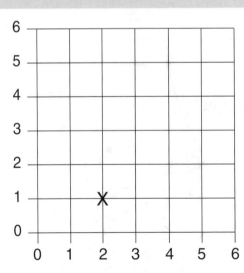

PAGE
TOTAL

11 Answer this sum.

 8.40 − 3.76 + 2.94 =

12 Turn the letter F through one right angle around the point X.
Move in a clockwise direction. Draw the new position.

You may use tracing paper.

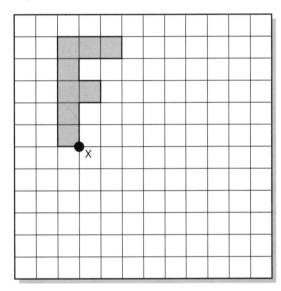

13 Use a ruler to measure the perimeter of this shape and write the answer.

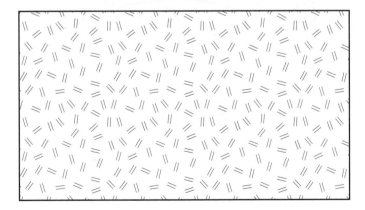

 Perimeter = cm

PAGE TOTAL

14 This table shows information about 100 people passing a school between 10.00 and 11.00 one morning.

About the people	Number of people
wearing spectacles	6
carrying an object	80
wearing a hat	9
pushing something	24

Draw a circle round the likelihood that someone wearing glasses will pass the school during the next minute.

certain   very likely   quite likely   unlikely   impossible

15 The graph shows the number of pupils in one school who were born in each month of the year.

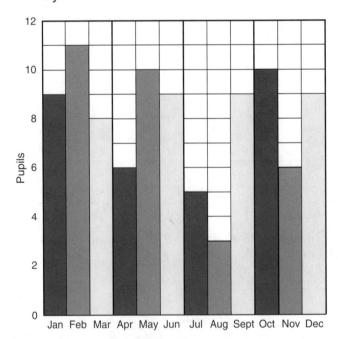

Fill in the table to show how many pupils were born in each quarter of the year.

Quarter year	Number
Jan – Mar	
Apr – Jun	
Jul – Sep	
Oct – Dec	

PAGE TOTAL

16

Answer this sum.

 342 x 26 = ☐

17

This machine multiplies numbers by 100.

8.3 in → 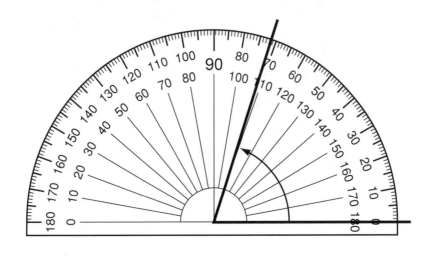 → out **830**

Finish the table.

in	0.35	5.04		
out			330	750

18

Measure the size of this angle.

☐ degrees

PAGE
TOTAL

19

At Highfields School there are 360 pupils.
Two-thirds of the pupils had perfect attendance during the summer term.

Write how many pupils this was.

 pupils

20

The diagram shows the type of cars passing the school gates between 10 and 10.30.

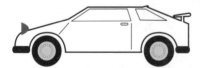

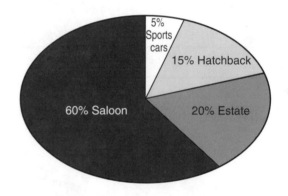

5% Sports cars

15% Hatchback

60% Saloon

20% Estate

40 estate cars passed.
Write how many saloon cars passed.

 saloon cars

PAGE TOTAL

• Test 4 •

Time started

Time finished

1 Write the total of this shopping list.

Oranges 3 kg at £1.30 a kg	£
Pears 2 kg at £2.10 a kg	£
Cherries 0.5 kg at £2.68 a kg	£
Potatoes 5 kg at £0.98 a kg	£
Total	£

2 Omar saves stickers.
He has 46 sports pictures and 38 pop star pictures.

Write how many stickers he has altogether.

 stickers.

3 These shapes have been sorted.

Write what the shapes have in common.

PAGE
TOTAL

4 The number 358 can be made using these three digits.

Write the largest number which can be made.

5 Pupils were asked the day of the week of their birthday.
This chart shows their results.

Day of the week	Sun	Mon	Tue	Wed	Thu	Fri	Sat
Number of pupils	8	5	10	12	9	3	5

Finish the bar graph to show this information.

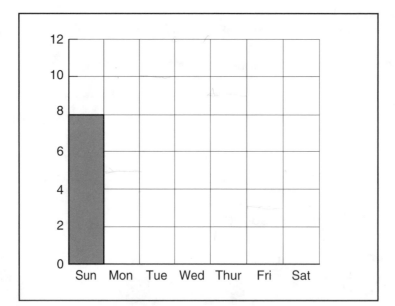

6 Write in the missing number.

$\div 100 = 53$

PAGE
TOTAL

7

Look at this pattern.

1 triangle  3 sticks

3 triangles  9 sticks

5 triangles  15 sticks

There is a rule for finding how many sticks are needed to make any number of triangles.

Write the rule.   *T = 3*

number of triangles ———→ (rule) ———→ number of sticks

8

This sum has a number missing from the box.

Write in the missing number in the box.

$\boxed{} \times 3 \div 4 = 6$

9

Estimate the area of this leaf in squares. Write your answer.

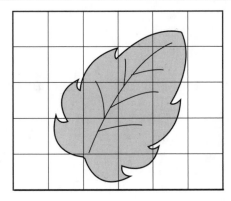

Area of the leaf is approximately $\boxed{}$ squares.

PAGE TOTAL

10 The co-ordinate of one vertex has been written in.

Write in the co-ordinates of the other two vertices.

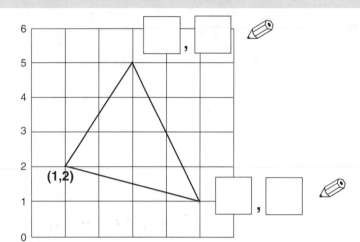

11 Draw the reflection of this shape.

You may use tracing paper.

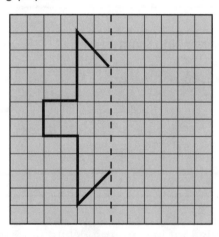

12 A slice has been taken from this pizza.

Write approximately what fraction of the pizza has been taken.

The slice is ⬚ of the pizza.

PAGE TOTAL

13

Class 4 were experimenting with rolling two dice and finding the total.
This table shows their results.

Dice score	Number of occurrences
2	6
3	10
4	21
5	41
6	68
7	64
8	56
9	32
10	16
11	13
12	9

Write which dice score is the mode.

14 The graph shows the weight of a baby during its first 12 weeks.

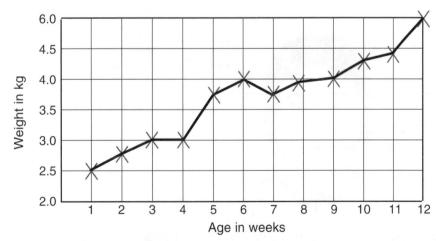

Age in weeks

Write how heavy the baby was after 6 weeks.

  kg

PAGE
TOTAL

15 Answer this sum.

$$782 \div 17 = \boxed{}$$

16 In a sale there is a 30% reduction in price.

Full price **£75.99**

Calculate the amount of reduction on this camera to the nearest penny.
Write your answer.

Amount of reduction = $\boxed{}$

17 Ann and Paul are playing a number guessing game.
Paul gives Ann a number which she changes using a rule.

I take
Paul's number and
multiply it by 7 then
subtract 2

Write a formula to work out the mystery number.

Use P for Paul's number and A for Ann's answer.

A = $\boxed{}$

PAGE
TOTAL

18 Draw a cross in each obtuse angle.

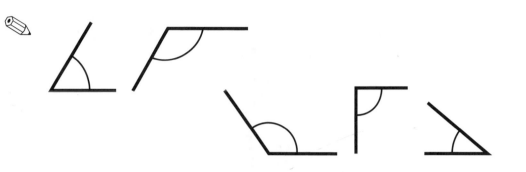

19 The pie chart shows the sales of items from Mrs Greg's newsagent's shop in one week.

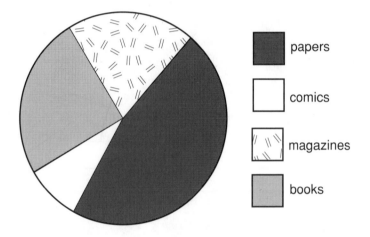

papers

comics

magazines

books

Mrs Greg made a total of £1000 during the week.

Write approximately how much she made selling books.

20 Write in the missing number.

$$5.93 + 3.72 - 1.85 = \boxed{}$$

PAGE
TOTAL

• Test 5 •

Time started [:]

Time finished [:]

1

Lee collects stamps.
Each page of her album holds ten stamps.

She has 126 pages full of stamps.

Write how many stamps she has.

 [ ]

2

Answer this sum.

$$7.21 - 2.83 + 3.88 = \boxed{}$$

[ ]

3

Write in the missing digit.

$$
\begin{array}{r}
6\ \square \\
\times\ \ 7 \\
\hline
4\ 4\ 8 \\
\end{array}
$$

[ ]

PAGE TOTAL

4 Write how much more water is needed to make the capacity up to 2 litres.

 ml

5 Tariq and Mandy measured the lengths of their friends' forefingers.

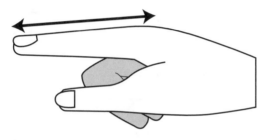

Here are their results:

5.2 cm   6.0 cm   8.0 cm   7.5 cm   8.0 cm   8.2 cm   5.5 cm

Write which length is the median.

 cm

6 The headteacher at Newton School is ordering packs of books for the new school year.

If one pack costs £3.32, write what 100 packs will cost.

PAGE TOTAL

7

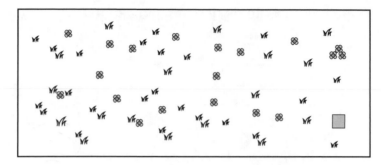

Carl, Emma and Arif conducted a worm count in the school field.
Carl marked out a square metre of field.
Emma found 17 worms in the square metre area.
Arif calculated the area of the field to be 128 square metres.

Write what they calculated the total number of worms to be.

8

Carl and Emma placed samples of soil in small boxes measuring 5.5 cm wide, 6.8 cm long and 3 cm deep.

3cm   6.8cm   5.5cm

They stored their sample boxes in a tray like this:

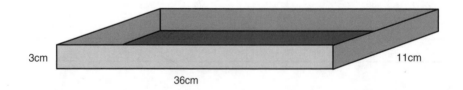

3cm   36cm   11cm

Calculate the largest number of sample boxes which will fit on their tray. Write your answer.

PAGE TOTAL

9

At a dog show 72 people were asked whether they had dogs.
Two-thirds of them said that they did.

Write how many people had dogs.

10

There is no remainder in this division.

Write in the missing digit.

$$7 \overline{)2 \boxed{} 9}$$

with quotient 3 7

11

Thomas and Jo Shipman were travelling down a motorway.
Thomas knew that the average speed in kilometres per hour is the total
number of kilometres travelled divided by the time taken in hours.

Write this out as a formula using:

S for the average speed in kilometres per hour
D for the distance in kilometres
T for the time in hours

12 Write in the missing number.

$$6 (2.46 + 3.58) = \boxed{}$$

13 The first table shows the temperature of some cities.

In the second table rewrite the order of the cities and temperatures.
Start with the warmest.

City	Temperature °C
Reykjavik	−12
Helsinki	−5
Moscow	−10
Stockholm	−8
Vienna	−3

City	Temp °C

14 Draw an angle of 76° at B.

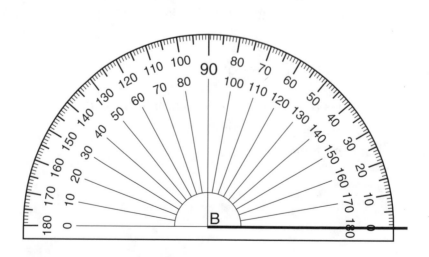

PAGE
TOTAL

15 Put a cross in all the obtuse angles.

16 The scale on this map is **1cm** to **5km**.

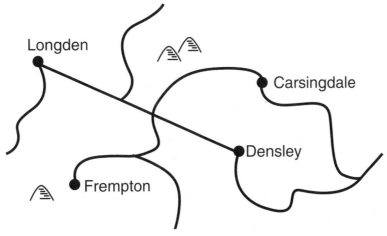

The distance measured on the map between Longden and Densley is 5.7 cm.

Write this distance in kilometres.

  km

17 Leslie collected money for a charity.
Here are the amounts which she collected.

Monday	Tuesday	Wednesday	Thursday	Friday	Saturday
£4.69	£7.96	£10.52	£5.65	£7.00	£9.56

Write the average daily amount she collected to the nearest penny.

PAGE TOTAL

18 Each quadrilateral has one or more lines of symmetry.

Draw the lines of symmetry on each shape.

   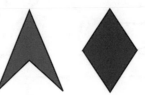

19 These coloured balls were placed in a bag:

12 green balls   2 red balls
4 yellow balls   2 blue balls

Estimate the chance that the first ball to be taken out of the bag will be a green one.

Draw an arrow on this probability scale to show your estimate.

     0   1

20 The graph shows the height of some children.

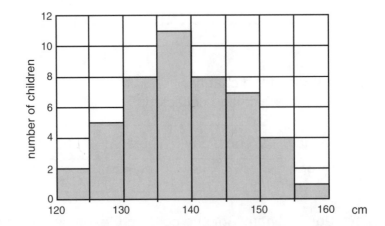

Write how many children are taller than 145 cm.

PAGE
TOTAL

Test 6

Time started [:]

Time finished [:]

1

316 people went to the school concert. They each paid 15p to enter.

Write how much money the school made.

2

Draw a ring round the number which is 100 times 37.

137   3007   3700   3070

3

Look at the shading on this badge.

$\frac{1}{4} \times \frac{25}{100}$

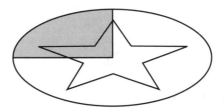

Write the approximate percentage which has been shaded.

PAGE TOTAL

4 This shape will look exactly the same after part of a turn.

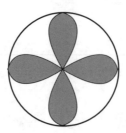

In a complete turn it will look exactly the same in 4 different positions.

Write how many different positions, during one turn, this shape will look exactly the same.

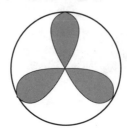

5 The area of this shape is 12 square units.

Write how many units long is its perimeter.

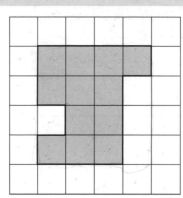

  units

6 100 packets of crayons costs £98.50.

Calculate the cost of 10 packets of crayons.

PAGE TOTAL

7

Write in the missing digit.

276 x 4 ☐ = 13,248

8

Nisa and Sue-Lee are playing a number game.

My rule is:
keep doubling the number
and subtracting 1.

Write the next two numbers Sue-Lee should say.

9   17   33

9

The price of a holiday was £360 each.
20% of the cost was for travel.

Write the travel cost for each person.

£130

PAGE
TOTAL

10 Here is a formula for finding the total cost of some books costing £5 each.

T = £5 x N
T = total price and **N** = number of books

Write a formula for finding the cost of 1 book when N books cost £45.

C =

C = cost for 1 book and **N** = number of books

11 Write in the missing number.

$$(6.73 - 4.89) \div 1.25 = \boxed{}$$

12 Here are some temperatures recorded in very cold places.

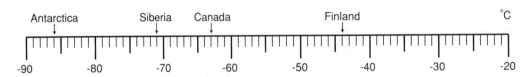

Write the temperature difference between Finland and Canada.

PAGE TOTAL

13 Here is how to find the cube of 12.

$$12^3 = 12 \times 12 \times 12$$
$$= 1728$$

Calculate the cube of 17.

$$17^3 = 17 \times 17 \times 17$$

---

14 The area of this rectangle is 304 cm². To find the area, the length was multiplied by the width.

19 cm

area = 304 cm²

 cm

Its length is 19 cm.

Calculate its width.

---

15 Each flag has one or more lines of symmetry.

Draw the lines of symmetry on each flag.

PAGE TOTAL

16 Here is a scale drawing of a whale.

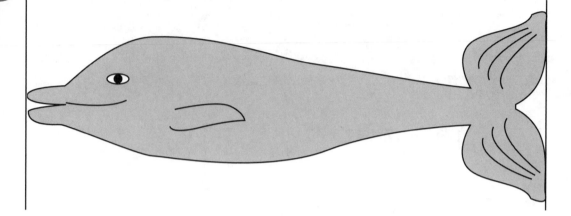

The scale of the drawing is **1 cm to 2 metres.**
Measure the drawing as accurately as you can.

Calculate the actual length of the whale. Write your answer.

17 Measure the size of this angle. Write down its size.

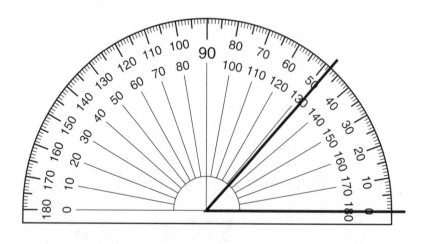

PAGE
TOTAL

18

Here are some amounts collected each day during a charity event.

£7.43	£9.55	£6.96	£10.75	£5.87	£4.78
Monday	Tuesday	Wednesday	Thursday	Friday	Saturday

Write the average amount collected each day, to the nearest penny.

19

In this game the arrow spins round and stops in one of the sections A to E.

Put a cross on the probability line to show the chance of the arrow stopping in section B.

```
0                                      1
|-------------------|------------------|
impossible                        certain
```

20

The pie chart shows the types of trees growing in a small wood.

- Oak
- Beech
- Pine
- Sycamore

Which tree is about three times as common as the beech tree?

PAGE TOTAL

• Test 7 •

Time started

Time finished

1 Pupils in a school were asked how many watched the early evening news on television last night. 15% of the 160 children said that they had.

Write how many children had watched the news on television.

2 Write in the missing digit.

$42 ÷ 17 = 26$

3 Here is an old thermometer which tells the temperature in degrees Fahrenheit. A short way of writing degrees Fahrenheit is °F.

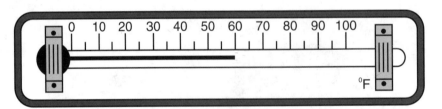

To find the approximate temperature in degrees Celsius use this simple formula.
Subtract 30 then halve the answer.

Change the °F temperature to °C. Write your answer.

PAGE
TOTAL

4 Write whether angle A is acute , obtuse or reflex.

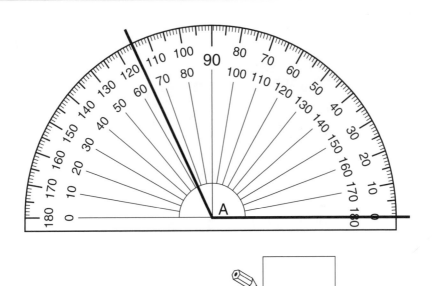

5 The chart shows the distances between cities in kilometres.

	Amsterdam	Berlin	Brussels	Florence	Madrid
Amsterdam		669	204	1391	1812
Berlin	669		781	1231	2378
Brussels	204	781		1197	1617
Florence	1391	1231	1197		1745
Madrid	1812	2378	1617	1745	

Write how far it is from Florence to Brussels.

 km

6 The decimal number **0.732** has been mapped to the number line.

Map the decimal number **0.477** to the number line.

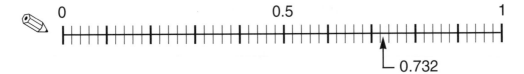

PAGE
TOTAL

7 There is a sale at the outdoor wear shop.

Full price **£67.50**

Firm step boots 30% off marked price

Calculate the sale price of the boots. Write your answer.

---

8 Write this fraction as a decimal.

$$\frac{7}{8} \ = \ \boxed{}$$

---

9 The instructions on a tin of paint advise diluting the first coat by adding water to the paint in the ratio:

2 parts of paint to 3 parts of water.

Write how much water is needed to dilute 500 ml of paint.

 ml

PAGE TOTAL

10

Ben was told that 10 square metres of material were used to cover a sofa. He tried to work out the length of the side of a square which had an area of 10 square metres.
His first estimate was 3.5 metres.
This was too large because   3.5 x 3.5 = 12.25.
His next estimate was 3.1 metres.
This was too small because   3.1 x 3.1 = 9.61.

Make a better estimate than Ben. Write your estimate.

   ☐   **X**   ☐   **=**   ☐

11

Solve this equation and write which number T stands for.

$$4T + 3 = T + 12$$

T =   ☐

12

Here is a building.
Jenna is standing on side A, looking at the end of the building.

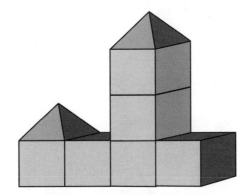

Tick which of these views she is looking at.

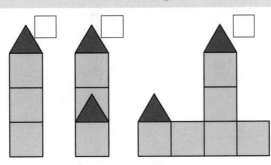

PAGE TOTAL

13 Draw the reflection of the triangle.
Label the corners of the reflected triangle A¹, B¹ and C¹

Write the co-ordinates of the reflected triangle.

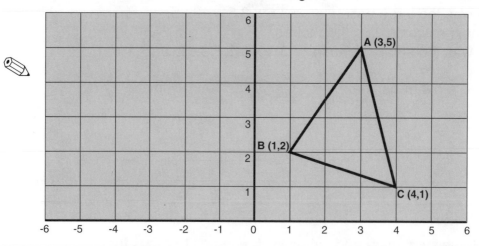

14 Tim's dictionary gives the definition of a parallelogram as follows:
Parallelogram – a quadrilateral which has both pairs of opposite sides parallel.

Put a tick inside each parallelogram.

15 On a building site were some wooden roof frames.

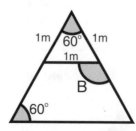

Work out the size of angle B. Write your answer.

PAGE
TOTAL

16 Rama is cutting out paper circles to make a festive decoration.
Each circle has a radius of 3.5 cm.

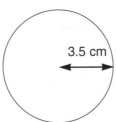

3.5 cm

Calculate the area of each circle. Write your answer.

In your calculations use $\pi = 3.14$ or $\dfrac{22}{7}$

17 Calculate the volume of this box.

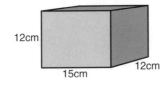

12cm

15cm   12cm

18 A survey was carried out at Sharlen Leisure Centre. The survey looked
at how often a group of 11 year old students attended during the year.

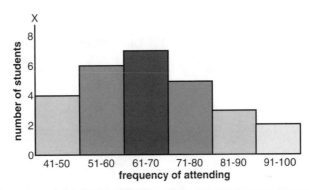

Write how many students attended more than 70 times a year.

PAGE TOTAL

19 This scatter graph shows the heights and shoe sizes of a group of students.

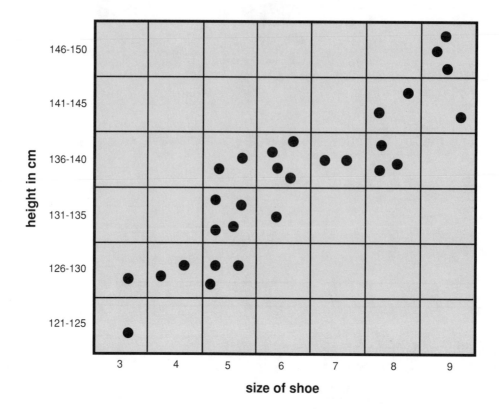

Write how many students take size 5 shoes and are under 136 cm tall.

20 There are 24 beads in a bag: 6 are yellow, 6 are red, 4 are green and the rest are blue.

What are the chances of taking out a blue bead?
Write down your answers.

PAGE TOTAL

• Answers to Test 1 •

1

in	2	4	**7**	**10**
out	**10**	**20**	35	50

2   **7 kg**

3   650   850

500 ——————————— 1000

4   **9 ounces**   **5**   **49 days**

6

9 2 25 16
8 6—12 30
14 5 17 24

7

210 **230** 300 **302** 310 **320** 340

8   **32°C**

9

2.5 kg of fruit at 60p a kg	£ **1.50**
3 kg of vegetables at 78p a kg	£ **2.34**
and 4 boxes at £1.45 each box.	£ **5.80**
Total	£ **9.64**

10   (ellipse, square, rhombus with symmetry lines)

11   **1300**   **12**   **9 cm**   **13**   **185**

14   5 6 + 1 7 - 1 7 = 56

15   15 40 45 35 20   are exactly divisible by 5

16   **50 minutes**   **17**   **5.85**

18   **35**

19

✓   ✓

20   **23 squares** (allow an error of 1 square either way)

TEST 1

8-11 questions correct	working towards Level 3
12-15 questions correct	satisfactory Level 3 standard
16-20 questions correct	good Level 3 standard, some Level 4

• Answers to Test 2 •

1 | 302 | 312 | 320 | 322 | 331 | 2   **650 ml**

3   **£3.20**   4   **8 boxes**   5   **48 cm**

6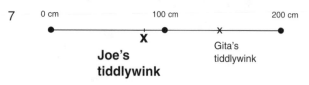

7
```
0 cm          100 cm              200 cm
●------------X----●------x--------●
             X              Gita's
          Joe's            tiddlywink
         tiddlywink
```

8   17   27   ⟨36⟩   42   ⟨47⟩   50   69

9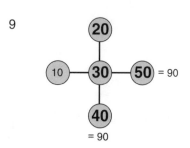

10   6 x 4 | ÷ | 3 = 8

11   17 x 10p =   1.70
     17 x 1p   = − 0.17
     ────────────
                £1.53

12   **They all contain right angles.**

13   **Length = 10 cm**

14   **33 vehicles**   15   **FRIDAY**

16
In	Out
16	4
48	**12**

17   **30 strides**

18 | **747** | cm

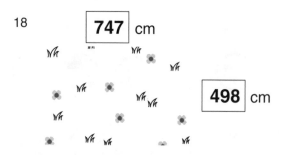

| **498** | cm

19

20   **9.00 am - 9.30 am**

TEST 2

8-11 questions correct	working towards Level 3
12-15 questions correct	satisfactory Level 3 standard
16-20 questions correct	good Level 3 standard, some Level 4

• Answers to Test 3 •

1   **115**   ÷ 5 = 23

2
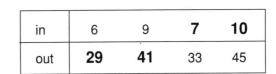

in	6	9	**7**	**10**
out	**29**	**41**	33	45

3

4

5   **Kapil**

6   **36**

7
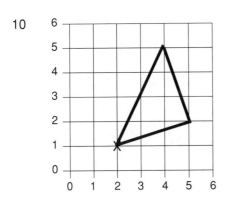

8   **£15**

9   **5** x **5** + **5** = 30

10
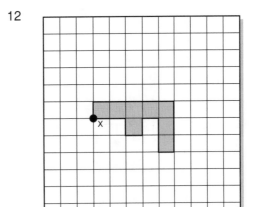

11   **7.58**

12

13   **28 cm**

14   (unlikely)

15

Quarter year	Number
Jan – Mar	**28**
Apr – Jun	**25**
Jul – Sep	**17**
Oct – Dec	**25**

16   **8,892**

17

in	0.35	5.04	**3.3**	**7.5**
out	**35**	**504**	330	750

18   **72 degrees**

19   **240 pupils**

20   **120 saloon cars**

TEST 3

5-11 questions correct	good Level 3 standard, some Level 4
12-15 questions correct	satisfactory Level 4 standard
16-20 questions correct	good Level 4 standard, some Level 5

• Answers to Test 4 •

1.

Oranges 3kg at £1.30 a kg	**£3.90**
Pears 2kg at £2.10 a kg	**£4.20**
Cherries 0.5kg at £2.68 a kg	**£1.34**
Potatoes 5kg at £0.98 a kg	**£4.90**
TOTAL	**£14.34**

2   **84 stickers**

3   **They all have a triangle face**

4   **853**

5.

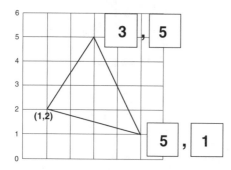

6.   **5,300**

7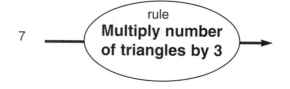

rule
Multiply number of triangles by 3

8   **8**   x 3 ÷ 4 = 6

9   **10 squares** (accept between 9 and 11)

10

3 , **5**

(1,2)

5 , **1**

11

12   **1/3**

13   **6**

14   **4.0 kg**

15   **46**

16   **£22.80**

17   **A = (Px7) − 2**

18

19   **£250**

20   **7.8**

TEST 4

5-11 questions correct	good Level 3 standard, some Level 4
12-15 questions correct	satisfactory Level 4 standard
16-20 questions correct	good Level 4 standard, some Level 5

• Answers to Test 5 •

1 **1,260**

2 **8.26**

3

	6	**4**
x		7
4	4	8

4 **600 ml**

5 **7.5 cm**

6 **£332**

7 **2,176**

8 **10**

9 **48**

10 **5**

11 **S = D ÷ T or S = D̲**
   **   T**

12 **36.24**

13

City	Temperature °C
Vienna	−3
Helsinki	−5
Stockholm	−8
Moscow	−10
Reykjavik	−12

14 **76°**

15

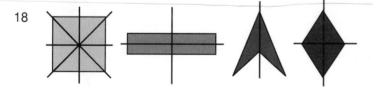

16 **28.5 km**

17 **£7.56**

18

19 0   1

20 **12**

TEST 5

5-11 questions correct	good Level 4 standard, some Level 5
12-15 questions correct	working towards Level 5 standard
16-20 questions correct	good Level 5 standard

• Answers to Test 6 •

1	**£47.40**	2	**3,700**	3	**25%**

4	**3**	5	**18 units**	6	**£9.85**

7   276 x 4 | **8** | = 13,248

8

9	**£72**	10	$C = \dfrac{45}{N}$ or 45 ÷ N

11   (6.73 - 4.89) ÷ 1.25 = | **1.472** | 12   **19°C**

13   **4,913**   14   width = | **16** | cm

15    16   **28.4 m**

17   **48°**   18   **£7.56**

19 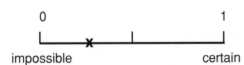   20   **Oak**

impossible   certain

TEST 6

5-11 questions correct	good Level 4 standard, some Level 5
12-15 questions correct	working towards Level 5 standard
16-20 questions correct	good Level 5 standard

• Answers to Test 7 •

1 **24**

2 **4** $42 \div 17 = 26$

3 **60°F is approximately 15°C**

4 **Obtuse**

5 **1,197 km**

6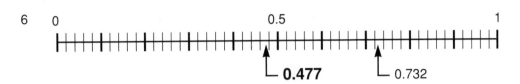
    0   0.5   1
    0.477   0.732

7 **£47.25**

8 $\frac{7}{8}$ = **0.875**

9 **750 ml**

10 **Any answer between 3.1 and 3.2**

11 **3**

12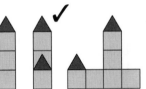

13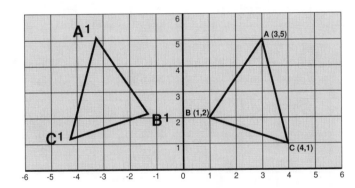

A^1 **-3** , **5**

B^1 **-1** , **2**

C^1 **-4** , **1**

14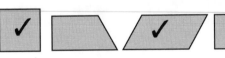

15 **120°**

16 **38.465 cm²**

17 **2160 cm³**

18 **10**

19 **7**

20 **1 in 3**

TEST 7

5-11 questions correct	good Level 5 standard, some Level 6
12-15 questions correct	working towards Level 6 standard
16-20 questions correct	good Level 6 standard

• Mathematics National Curriculum Record •

TEST 1

	Level 3 N&A	Level 3 S&M	Level 3 HD	Level 4 N&A	Level 4 S&M	Level 4 HD
1	■					
2		■				
3	■					
4		■				
5	■					
6	■					
7		■				
8		■				
9	■					
10						
11		■				
12			■			
13		■				
14	■					
15	■					
16				■		
17				■		
18					■	
19					■	
20					■	

TEST 2

	Level 3 N&A	Level 3 S&M	Level 3 HD	Level 4 N&A	Level 4 S&M	Level 4 HD
1	■					
2		■				
3	■					
4	■					
5	■					
6	■					
7		■				
8		■				
9		■				
10						
11		■				
12	■					
13		■				
14			■			
15						
16				■		
17					■	
18					■	
19					■	
20						■

TEST 3

	Level 3 N&A	Level 3 S&M	Level 3 HD	Level 4 N&A	Level 4 S&M	Level 4 HD	Level 5 N&A	Level 5 S&M	Level 5 HD
1	■								
2	■								
3	■								
4		■							
5			■						
6				■					
7				■					
8				■					
9				■					
10				■					
11				■					
12					■				
13					■				
14						■			
15						■			
16							■		
17							■		
18							■		
19								■	
20									■

TEST 4

	Level 3 N&A	Level 3 S&M	Level 3 HD	Level 4 N&A	Level 4 S&M	Level 4 HD	Level 5 N&A	Level 5 S&M	Level 5 HD
1	■								
2	■								
3	■								
4		■							
5			■						
6				■					
7				■					
8				■					
9				■					
10					■				
11					■				
12				■					
13				■					
14						■			
15									
16							■		
17							■		
18							■		
19								■	
20								■	

• Mathematics National Curriculum Record •

TEST 5 / TEST 6 (Levels 4 and 5)

	Level 4				Level 5		
	Number & Algebra	Shape & Measures	Handling data		Number & Algebra	Shape & Measures	Handling data
TEST 5							
1	▓						
2							
3	▓						
4		▓					
5			▓				
6					▓		
7					▓		
8						▓	
9					▓		
10					▓		
11					▓		
12					▓		
13					▓		
14						▓	
15						▓	
16						▓	
17						▓	
18							▓
19							▓
20							▓
TEST 6							
1	▓						
2	▓						
3	▓						
4		▓					
5		▓					
6					▓		
7					▓		
8					▓		
9					▓		
10					▓		
11					▓		
12					▓		
13					▓		
14						▓	
15						▓	
16						▓	
17						▓	
18							▓
19							▓
20							▓

TEST 7 (Levels 4, 5 and 6)

	Level 4				Level 5				Level 6		
	Number & Algebra	Shape & Measures	Handling data		Number & Algebra	Shape & Measures	Handling data		Number & Algebra	Shape & Measures	Handling data
TEST 7											
1					▓						
2					▓						
3					▓						
4						▓					
5							▓				
6									▓		
7									▓		
8									▓		
9									▓		
10									▓		
11									▓		
12										▓	
13										▓	
14										▓	
15										▓	
16										▓	
17										▓	
18											▓
19											▓
20											

Using this Record

This chart can be used to build up a record of a child's strengths and weaknesses in the three attainment targets in mathematics – and at what Levels.

More detailed information can be gained by reference to the topics being assessed by each of the questions.

Pupil achievement record

Write how many you scored in each test.

TEST 1 ☐

TEST 2 ☐

TEST 3 ☐

TEST 4 ☐

TEST 5 ☐

TEST 6 ☐

TEST 7 ☐

GRAND TOTAL ☐

Mark your grand total on the Achievement Line. Try colouring it in after you have marked each test.

0

10

} working towards level 3

20

} good level 3

30

} excellent level 3, some level 4

40

50

50

} working towards level 4

60

} good level 4

70

80

} excellent level 4, some level 5

90

100

100

} working towards level 5

110

} good level 5

120

130

} excellent level 5, some level 6

140

Well done!